Acknowledgements

This book was made with equal parts love and heartache. What started as a simple conversation between a chef and a frustrated son turned into a movement. A literal army of volunteers- doctors, agencies, magazines, lawyers, more chefs, publishers, designers, editors, photographers, daughters, mothers, sons, fathers, grandparents- all with the single mission to use food as a weapon in the battle against cancer.

It's here we say this book could never have happened without you. It's here we say because of you, we're just getting started. There's so much more to do. It's here we say sorry. Because this book is too late for some. But may help save others.

It's here we say fuck cancer.

And it's here we say we're going to win. Not in time for everyone. But in time.

From everything we have. Thank you.

How to use this book

This collection of recipes was created by award-winning chefs, most of whom battled cancer already one way or another. That said, there are no silver bullets. Some of these creations are going to taste magical, others may not be just what the doctor ordered. It will be different for everyone and may even change for the individual depending on their stage of treatment. Use "The Chemo Kitchen Cookbook" as a baseline. But try different things. Rotate in favorite ingredient substitutions. Find what works and keep doing it. The little victories mount up.

Food group key:

 FRUITS

 GRAINS

 VEGGIES

 MEAT

 DAIRY

 SUGARS

What is happening, anyway?

Chemotherapy targets fast-growing cells. Which is good if you are hunting cancer, but not so good if you are a hair follicle or taste bud.

Our doctors told us the taste buds in our mouths are no more than three weeks old. The young ones learn from the senior citizens. When you wipe out the taste bud population, for some people, all memory of flavor goes with it. Which is why your favorite food one night can taste like sand just a few treatments later. Weirder, some people don't have any problems and others lose taste completely.

There are some homeopathic solutions in our pages, but really the main purpose of this book is to just get people inspired to eat again. Deliciousness is a pleasant side effect. Whether you are in treatment or a caregiver, we're sorry you're going through this. But we are here to help.

Salads & Snacks

Geoff Tracy of Chef Geoff's

Super Kale Salad 11

Ethan Stowell

Panzanella 13

Delicata Squash with Chestnut Honey 15

Carrie Nahabedian of NAHA

Freshmade Ricotta Salad with Asparagus, Fava Bean &
Candied Lemon 17

Charred Melon Salad with Prawns 19

Stuart Brioza of State Bird Provisions

Persian Cucumbers with Kinako Dressing 21

Matthew Buchanan of Leaning Pear

Panzanella with Fresh Mozzarella 23

Kale-Smoked Gouda Fundido Dip 25

Eric Tanaka of Tom Douglas

Trofie Pasta Salad 27

Chris Shepherd of Underbelly

Crispy Seasonal Veggies with Caramelized Fish Sauce 29

Matthew Fortner of Tom Douglas

Wild Salmon Gravlax 31

Edmond Sanctis of Sahale Snacks

Tumeric-Boosted Berry Nut Mix 33

Entrées

Tom Douglas & Brock Johnson

Sweet Pea Soup with Pea Vines & Radish 35

Kitchen Sink Fried Rice 37

Matthew Buchanan of Leaning Pear

Hearty Spanish-Style Lentil & Chorizo Soup 39

Indoor Pulled Chicken with Sweet & Tangy BBQ Sauce 41

Eric Tanaka of Tom Douglas

#1 Miso Matzo Ball Soup 43

Mary Ann Esposito of *Ciao Italia*

Zuppa Pavese (Pavia's Poached Egg Soup) 45

Spaghetti Alla Carbonara (Coal Miner-Style) 47

Skye Craig of *MasterChef Australia*

Blissful Pea Coriander & Coconut Soup 49

Blake Pope of Kindered

Red Curry Sweet Potato Soup 51

Chris Shepherd of Underbelly

Pork Belly & Kimchi Stew 53

Charred Chicken over Papaya Salad 55

Rice-Seared Trout w/ Mandarin Hazelnut Brown Butter 57

Michou Cornu

Chicken Thigh Roulade with Mushroom & Tarragon Jus 59

Filet with Spinach 61

Entrées continued

Jennifer Jasinski of Rioja

Colorado Lamb Dip on Goat Cheese Biscuits 63

Seisuke Kamimura

Turkey Meatloaf (Freezable) 67

Thierry Rautureau of Loulay and Luc

Baked Salmon with Hazelnut Gremolata 69

Shaun McCrain of Copine

White Beans & Clams 71

Brady Williams of Canlis

Dungeness Crab with Fresh Corn Polenta 73

Desserts

Hot Cakes

Grilled Chocolate Sandwich with Salted Caramel Sauce 75

Stuart Lane of Spinasse

Cucumber Panna Cotta 77

Skye Craig of *Master Chef Australia*

Two-Minute Fig, Walnut & Bee Pollen Ice Cream 79

Nicki Kerbs of Cupcake Royale

Goodship Pot Chocolate Fondue 81

Goodship Pot Chocolate Cheesecake 83

Goodship Snickerdoodle Apple Crisp 85

Beverages

Skye Craig of *Master Chef Australia*

Antioxidant Berry Smoothie 87

Belly Healer Juice 89

Tom Macy of Clover Club

Banana Breeze 91

Ginger & Mint Spiked Arnold Palmer 93

Super Kale Salad

by Geoff Tracy

DRESSING

18 ounces plain yogurt

2 tablespoons fresh lime juice

1/2 cup honey

2 tablespoons extra-virgin olive oil

1/4 cup fresh lemon juice

2 teaspoons kosher salt

SALAD

2 heads Tuscan kale, roughly chopped

1/2 head purple kale, roughly chopped

1 pint blueberries

6 ounces dried cranberries

1 large carrot, peeled and grated

2 cups granola (or chopped granola bars)

1/2 cup red onion, diced small

1/2 cup sunflower seeds

1 teaspoon kosher salt

1/2 teaspoon ground black pepper

1 cup honey yogurt dressing

Food groups

Servings

4+

MAKE THE DRESSING

1. Place the yogurt and the other ingredients in a medium-sized bowl, and whisk for 1 to 2 minutes.

ASSEMBLE THE SALAD

2. In a large bowl, combine all salad ingredients

3. Add the dressing and mix thoroughly with gloved hands or a pair of tongs.

4. Divide salad among 4 serving bowls.

COOKING TIPS

This salad is great on its own or paired with a few grilled shrimp or a 6-ounce portion of sautéed salmon.

You can use light or fat-free yogurt for a healthier dressing. The dressing will keep for up to 10 days in an airtight container in the refrigerator.

Panzanella

by Ethan Stowell

INGREDIENTS

1/2 baguette, cubed

7 tablespoons extra-virgin olive oil

kosher salt and cracked pepper

4 ounces fresh green beans, trimmed

8 oil-packed anchovy fillets, chopped

1 clove garlic, thinly sliced

1/2 pound ripe heirloom tomatoes, cut into large chunks

juice of 1 lemon

1/4 red onion

Food groups

Servings

6+

DIRECTIONS

1. Preheat the oven to 350°F. Bring a pot of water to a boil and prepare an ice-water bath for the beans

2. Toss the bread cubes with 3 tablespoons of the olive oil and season with salt and pepper. Bake until slightly dry but still chewy in the center, about 15 minutes.

3. Place the anchovies and garlic in a large bowl with the remaining 4 tablespoons olive oil and a pinch of salt and pepper. Add the tomatoes and lemon juice. Shave the onion on a mandoline and add to the mixture.

4. Add the bread cubes and allow to sit for 10 to 15 minutes, stirring occasionally.

5. To serve, divide the panzanella among 6 shallow bowls.

Delicata Squash
with Chestnut Honey

by Ethan Stowell

INGREDIENTS

2 delicata squash, about 1 to 1 1/2 pounds

2 tablespoons extra-virgin olive oil

kosher salt and cracked pepper

2 tablespoons Tuscan chestnut honey, or your favorite honey

2 tablespoons unsalted butter

Food groups

Servings

4

DIRECTIONS

1. Preheat the oven to 375°F.

2. Cut off the ends of each squash and split lengthwise. Scoop out the seeds with a spoon. Cut each half horizontally into 3/4- to 1-inch slices. The slices should resemble half-moons.

3. Divide the olive oil between 2 sauté pans large enough to hold the squash in a single layer. Heat the pans over high heat until the oil is almost smoking. Brown the squash on both sides until deep golden brown, 3 to 4 minutes per side.

4. Transfer the squash to paper towels to drain. While still hot, season with salt and pepper.

5. Arrange the squash in a single layer in a small baking dish, drizzle with the honey, and dot with the butter. Bake for 15 to 20 minutes to finish cooking the squash and heat through.

COOKING TIPS

This dish can be prepared up to the point of putting it in the oven. The squash can sit on the counter for a few hours before baking, while you finish cooking the rest of the meal.

Freshmade Ricotta Salad
with Asparagus, Fava Bean & Candied Lemon

by Carrie Nahabedian

RICOTTA

1 gallon whole milk

2 cups buttermilk

SALAD

2 bunches asparagus

2 pounds fava beans

2 lemons

1/2 cup simple syrup

salt and cracked pepper

extra-virgin olive oil

red wine vinegar

1 bunch chervil

Food groups

Servings

2

MAKING THE RICOTTA

1. Put the milk and buttermilk into a heavy stainless-steel pot and bring to a slight boil. Reduce heat and simmer for 5 minutes. Season with kosher salt to taste.

2. Ladle the cheese into a bowl through cheesecloth, and let cheese drain until it is no longer dripping.

3. Use immediately or refrigerate. The cheese will last up to 2 days. For ricotta that can be served crumbled, cold or warm, let cool and place into a plastic container. You can also form the soft ricotta into shapes by spooning it into molds while warm.

COOKING TIPS

For richer flavor, swap whole milk for fresh goat's milk.

WINE PAIRING

We recommend serving this salad with a 2002 Matanzas Creek Sauvignon Blanc from Sonoma County. This Sauvignon Blanc with a hint of both Sémillon and Sauvignon Musqué has bright color and aroma with a soft floral character. It highlights citrus fruits, with flavors of fig, pink grapefruit, and lemon. The bright fruit and acidity are perfect with this spring salad.

PREPARE THE SALAD

4. Trim the bottom of the asparagus and peel, if desired, from the tip to the bottom. Blanch in a large pot of boiling salted water until tender. Plunge immediately into an ice bath to refresh. Remove from the water, pat dry, and set aside.

5. Pop the fava beans out of their pods and blanch quickly in the same blanching water as the asparagus. Refresh in an ice bath and peel the fava beans from their inner shell "skin." Set aside.

6. Peel the lemon with a peeler, taking care not to take the pith. Wash under cold water to remove any oils. Blanch the peel quickly in hot water, refresh in an ice bath, and then place in a small saucepot and cover with the simple syrup. Cook until tender over a slow flame, approximately 30 minutes. Remove from heat, cool, and julienne. Reserve lemon peel and a little of the au jus. Candied lemon peel has a multitude of uses.

7. Toss the asparagus and fava beans with a touch of extra-virgin olive oil and vinegar. Season to taste. Place on the serving plate. Spoon the warm ricotta cheese on top, drizzle with a little of the lemon peel jus and candied lemon peel, and sprinkle with chervil.

Charred Melon Salad
with Prawns

by Carrie Nahabedian

INGREDIENTS

1 cantaloupe, ripe

1/4 seedless red watermelon

1/4 yellow watermelon

1/4 cup extra-virgin olive oil

8 ounces apple juice

1 red bell pepper, medium dice

1 yellow bell pepper, medium dice

1 red onion, medium dice

1 ounce red wine vinegar

2 ounces walnut oil

2 ounces basil, chiffonade

2 ounces chives, cut small

16 prawns with heads on (or shelled shrimp)

Food groups

Servings

4

DIRECTIONS

1. Peel the cantaloupe and watermelon and cut into thick 1/2-inch slices. Remove all the seeds. Lightly coat the slices with the olive oil and, over a medium-high grill, grill the melon slices quickly to a nice glow of color. Do not grill them too much, or they will become soft and mushy in texture. Set aside to cool.

2. Cook the apple juice in a saucepot over medium-high heat until reduced by one half. Lightly cook the peppers and onion in the juice. Cool the mixture.

3. Dice the grilled melon into large pieces. When both the melon and pepper and onion mixture are chilled, mix the melons in with the pepper and onion mixture.

4. Add the red wine vinegar, walnut oil, basil, and chives.

5. Season the salad with kosher salt and cracked black pepper and chill.

6. Place a ring mold on a plate, fill it with the charred melon salad, and top with the prawns.

Persian Cucumbers
with Kinako Dressing

by Stuart Brioza

CUCUMBERS

4 crunchy Persian cucumbers, cut into irregular 1 x 1/2 x 1/2 inch pieces

1 tablespoon kosher salt

2 teaspoons grated ginger

1/4 cup black sesame seeds, toasted

1/4 teaspoon Maldon or other flaky sea salt

extra kinako powder for sprinkling

SAUCE

1 cup kinako powder (ground roasted soybeans)

2 teaspoons kosher salt

1 teaspoon powdered ginger

1/2 cup plus 2 tablespoons grapeseed oil

1/2 cup plus 2 tablespoons toasted sesame oil

1/4 cup rice vinegar

Food groups

Servings

4

DIRECTIONS

1. To make the dressing, whisk together the kinako powder, salt, and ginger in a mixing bowl. Slowly pour in the oils and vinegar, whisking constantly until the dressing is well combined.

2. Half an hour before serving the dish, combine the Persian cucumbers, salt, and ginger to extract any excess liquid. Strain the cucumbers through a fine mesh sieve and reserve until ready to use.

3. Combine the sesame seeds and Maldon salt in a mortar and pound until the mixture resembles coarsely ground black pepper.

4. Pour about 1/4 cup of the dressing on a large platter. Arrange the cucumbers on the bed of dressing, sprinkle on 1 tablespoon of kinako powder, and sprinkle on about 1 tablespoon of the sesame mixture. Serve right away.

Panzanella
with Fresh Mozzarella

by Matthew Buchanan

INGREDIENTS

1/4 cup cherry tomatoes, halved

1/2 cup cucumber, sliced

3 ounces fresh mozzarella

3 basil leaves, chopped

1/4 cup olives

1/4 cup red onion, sliced

stale, good-quality rustic bread (sourdough, baguette, etc.)

good olive oil, to taste

red wine vinegar, to taste

Food groups

Servings

4

DIRECTIONS

1. Combine the first 6 ingredients in a large mixing bowl.

2. Take three or four 1-inch-thick slices of the bread, sprinkle them with a little olive oil, and either grill them (my personal preference), broil them, or toast them in a toaster oven. A little char is a good thing, but don't dry them out completely.

3. Cut the bread into large cubes and throw the cubes in the bowl with all of the other ingredients.

4. Add about 1 tablespoon vinegar and 2 to 3 tablespoons of olive oil—or as much as you like.

5. Toss everything together well and let the bread soak up the juices. Finish with a little sea salt and cracked pepper.

Kale-Smoked Gouda
Fundido Dip

by Matthew Buchanan

INGREDIENTS

1 bunch kale, chopped

8 ounces cream cheese

5 ounces smoked Gouda, shredded

3 ounces sour cream

1/2 teaspoon salt

1/2 teaspoon pepper

1 clove garlic, minced

Food groups

Servings

4

DIRECTIONS

1. Bring a pot of lightly salted water to a boil and blanch the kale for about 3 minutes.

2. Meanwhile, combine the cheeses, sour cream, salt, pepper, and garlic in a stand mixer and beat with a paddle attachment until combined. (You could use a food processor as well.)

3. When the kale is done, drain it and squeeze some of the excess water out with the back of a wooden spoon or spatula. Toss it in the bowl with the cheese mixture and mix until combined.

4. You can serve the dip as is or put it in a ramekin with a little parmesan cheese on top and broil it until golden brown on top. Serve with pita, crackers, or whatever strikes your fancy.

Trofie Pasta Salad

by Eric Tanaka

DASHI (BROTH)

3 dried shiitake mushrooms

1 clove garlic

2 ginger coins (round slices)

1 quart water

1 sheet dried seaweed

PASTA

2 tablespoons soy sauce

1 cup water

3 ounces dried trofie (a short, thin, twisted pasta)

4 tablespoons olive oil

3 cloves garlic, sliced

1/4 bulb fennel, cut into 3/4-inch squares

1/2 zucchini, cut into thin half-moons

2 ounces broccoli florets

2 tablespoons za'atar spice

2 ounces sugar snap peas

grated parmesan cheese, to taste

Food groups

Servings

2

DIRECTIONS

1. Simmer the shiitakes, garlic, ginger, and water for 30 minutes. Strain; remove the shiitakes, slice, and reserve. Steep the dried sheet of seaweed in the dashi for 30 minutes.

2. Add soy sauce and 1 cup of water to pot.

3. Bring the dashi to a boil and add dried trofie pasta. Cook until pasta is al dente.

4. In a sauté pan, sweat olive oil with sliced garlic over low heat.

5. Add fennel, zucchini, broccoli, and the shiitakes from the dashi.

6. Cook slowly over medium-low heat for 45 minutes, stirring occasionally.

7. Season with salt, pepper, and za'atar.

8. Add cooked pasta while still hot, along with peas. Toss thoroughly and serve in 2 bowls. Top with parmesan cheese.

Crispy Seasonal Veggies
with Caramelized Fish Sauce

by Chris Shepherd

SAUCE

2 tablespoons rice wine vinegar

3/4 cup fish sauce

1 1/2 tablespoons brown sugar

1 garlic clove

10 sprigs cilantro

1 tablespoon water

VEGGIES

Neutral vegetable oil

32 ounces seasonal vegetables

1/2 cup Underbelly fish sauce (see sauce recipe)

2 tablespoons chopped cilantro

juice from 1/2 lime

4 cilantro leaves for garnish (optional)

Food groups

Servings

4

ROAST THE VEGGIES

1. Fill a large pot or Dutch oven with enough oil to completely submerge vegetables and heat to 350°F.

2. While the oil is coming to temperature, heat a large skillet on high heat until it is very hot. When you're almost ready to fry the vegetables, add the fish sauce into the skillet. It should sizzle and come to an almost instant boil.

3. Cook until the sauce reduces by half.

4. Meanwhile, carefully add the vegetables to the oil and fry until tender, but still crispy— roughly 30 seconds to a minute.

5. Transfer the vegetables to a paper-towel-lined plate to drain, then quickly add them to the skillet with the fish sauce. Add the lime juice and chopped cilantro. Toss to coat the vegetables in the sauce.

6. Divide among 4 bowls or plates and garnish with the cilantro leaves.

MAKE THE SAUCE

7. In a saucepot over medium heat, brown the olive oil and reserved lamb trimmings.

8. Add the shallots and garlic and cook until golden. Then add the tomatoes and stir until pulpy. Add thyme and peppercorns, then deglaze the pan with red wine. Reduce until the wine is syrupy.

9. Add the veal demiglace to the pot and bring it to a simmer, skimming the impurities away as needed until the flavors have melded and the sauce is a desirable consistency to coat the lamb. Strain the sauce through a fine-mesh strainer and season to taste with salt and pepper. Hold warm until ready to sauce cooked lamb.

Wild Salmon Gravlax

by Matthew Fortner

CURE

2/3 cup kosher salt

2/3 cup granulated sugar

1/4 cup packed brown sugar

1 1/2 teaspoons paprika

1 teaspoon ground fennel seeds

1/4 teaspoon cayenne

SALMON

1 1/4 pounds salmon fillet, preferably wild, preferably skin on, pin bones removed

Food groups

Servings

2

DIRECTIONS

1. Combine the cure ingredients in a small bowl. Sprinkle the bottom of a glass or other non-reactive pan, with about 1/2 inch of the cure and place the fish in the pan, skin side down. Blanket the fish with the remaining cure, which should form a layer about 1 1/2 inches thick.

2. Cover the salmon with a piece of wax paper and another smaller pan, then weigh it down with a few cans. Store in the refrigerator for 2 to 3 days until the salmon is quite firm to the touch; the exact amount of time will depend on how thick your piece of salmon is.

3. Remove the wax paper and the cans, then use a rubber spatula to scrape the cure from the salmon. Remove the salmon from the pan and briefly rinse it, then pat it dry with paper towels. Slice the salmon very thinly on the bias.

Gravlax is not difficult to make, but curing is a two- or three-day process, so plan accordingly. It's best to use a piece of salmon that is no more than an inch or two thick; a thicker piece will take longer to cure. A salmon fillet with the skin on will help you slice the gravlax paper-thin after it is cured. Gravlax will keep for a week, covered in plastic wrap, in the refrigerator.

— Matthew Fortner of Tom Douglas

COOKING TIPS

Use a spice grinder or a clean coffee grinder for grinding the spices.

Tumeric-Boosted Berry
Nut Mix

by Edmond Sanctis

INGREDIENTS

1 tablespoon coconut oil

2 tablespoons coconut sugar

2 tablespoons pure maple syrup

1 cup raw pecan halves or pieces

1 cup raw cashews

1/2 cup dried cranberries

1/2 cup dried blueberries

2 teaspoons Ceylon cinnamon

1 teaspoon turmeric powder

1/2 teaspoon sea salt

Food groups

Servings

2-4

DIRECTIONS

1. Preheat oven to 350° F. Line a large baking sheet with parchment paper.

2. Combine coconut oil, coconut sugar, and maple syrup in a large pan or skillet and cook over medium heat until it starts to bubble. Stir and simmer the liquid for one minute. Add the nuts, and stir well to coat evenly. Remove from heat and stir in cranberries, blueberries, cinnamon, turmeric, and salt.

3. Evenly distribute the nut and berry mix on the lined baking sheet and bake for 7 to 8 minutes.

4. Cool for 20 minutes and toss with a dash of sea salt. Store in a sealed container.

Healthy snacking is a great way to add nutrition to your diet, especially when you don't feel like eating a big meal. Tree nuts are an excellent healthy snack. They contain many nutrients, such as protein, fiber, plant sterols, omega-3 fatty acids, micronutrients (such as copper and magnesium), and antioxidants (such as vitamin E), that support healthy tissues.

This mix is boosted with turmeric, recognized as having many therapeutic benefits, and sweetened with coconut sugar—one of the lowest glycemic index sweeteners—providing more sustained energy. Add fresh Brazil nuts to add to the mix, as they are an excellent source of selenium.

— Edmond Sanctis of Sahale Snacks

Sweet Pea Soup
with Pea Vines & Radish

by Tom Douglas & Brock Johnson

SOUP

1 tablespoon olive oil

3/4 cup celery, chopped

1 cup onion, chopped

3/4 cup leeks, white part only, thinly sliced

4 cups chicken stock or vegetable stock

1 sprig fresh thyme

2 cups sugar snap peas, thinly sliced

4 cups fresh English sweet peas, shelled

2 cups lightly packed flat-leaf parsley leaves

kosher or sea salt and cracked pepper, to taste

GARNISH

1 cup pea shoots, root ends trimmed off

1/4 cup thinly sliced radishes

1/2 lemon, as needed

extra-virgin olive oil, as needed

kosher or sea salt and cracked pepper to taste

Food groups

Servings

5-6

DIRECTIONS

1. Put the olive oil in a large saucepan over medium heat. When the oil is warm, add the celery, onion, and leek. Lower the heat and cook the vegetables, stirring, until softened but not browned, about 15 minutes.

2. Add the stock and thyme sprig. Bring to a boil, then lower heat to a simmer and simmer for 15 minutes. Discard the thyme sprig. Strain the soup and puree the solids in a food processor or blender, using as much soup liquid as needed to get a smooth puree. Keep solids and liquid separate and chill both over an ice bath.

3. Meanwhile, bring a large pot of salted water to the boil. Add the sugar snap peas and boil 3 minutes. Add the English peas and cook 3 or 4 minutes more. Drain the peas into a colander and plunge into an ice bath. Drain.

4. In another pot of boiling salted water, cook the parsley for 1 minute. Drain, plunge into an ice bath, and drain again. Squeeze the parsley leaves to remove excess moisture.

5. In a food processor or blender, puree the peas and parsley using as much of the pureed soup liquid as necessary to get a smooth puree. Combine the pea-parsley puree with the pureed soup vegetables and add as much of the soup liquid as needed to bring soup to consistency (you will use most or all of the liquid). Pass the soup through a fine strainer, scraping the solids to get as much through as possible, or through a food mill. Season soup to taste with salt and pepper (about 2 teaspoons salt and 1/8 teaspoon pepper, depending on how much you salted the blanching water).

6. To make the garnish, combine pea shoots and radishes in a bowl. Squeeze some juice from the lemon over it, add some olive oil, and toss. Season to taste with salt and pepper.

7. Gently reheat soup and serve hot with a little mound of pea shoot and radish salad on top of each bowl of soup.

Kitchen Sink Fried Rice

by Tom Douglas

RICE

2 to 4 tablespoons vegetable oil, as needed

1/3 cup thinly sliced lup chong (sweet Chinese sausage)

3 green onions, chopped, white and green parts

3 cups cooked brown or white rice, chilled overnight

1/2 cup kimchi, drained and chopped into 1-inch pieces

2 tablespoons soy sauce

2 tablespoons rice wine vinegar

2 tablespoons mirin

1 1/2 cups bean sprouts

TOPPINGS

3/4 pound sashimi-grade raw fish, such as ahi tuna, thinly sliced

2 avocados, peeled, pitted, and sliced

Black lava sea salt

Food groups

Servings

2

FRY THE RICE

1. Heat a large heavy skillet or seasoned wok over medium-high heat and add 2 tablespoons of oil.

2. When the oil is hot, add the lup chong and green onions and fry, stirring, for a minute. Add the rice and toss to coat with the oil. (Add a little more oil if needed.)

3. Continue to fry the rice, stirring and tossing occasionally, but allowing the rice enough time to stay in contact with the hot pan to crisp and brown. When the rice is browned, add the kimchi, soy, vinegar, and mirin and stir-fry the mixture until hot, stirring and tossing the ingredients to combine. Add the bean sprouts, toss to combine, then remove from the heat.

ASSEMBLE

4. Put the fried rice on plates. Top each portion first with slices of avocado, then with slices of raw fish. Sprinkle lightly with sea salt and serve.

COOKING NOTES

Be mindful when preparing and consuming raw fish during chemotherapy. Ensure it is clean and not cross-contaminated.

Hearty Spanish-Style
Lentil & Chorizo Soup

by Matthew Buchanan

INGREDIENTS

1 pound (2 1/4 cups) lentils, picked over and rinsed

salt and pepper

1 large onion

5 tablespoons extra-virgin olive oil

1 1/2 pounds Spanish-style chorizo sausage, pricked with fork several times

3 carrots, peeled and cut into 1/4-inch pieces

3 tablespoons fresh parsley, minced

7 cups water, plus extra as needed

3 tablespoons sherry vinegar, plus extra for seasoning

2 bay leaves

1/8 teaspoon ground cloves

2 tablespoons sweet smoked paprika

3 garlic cloves, minced

1 tablespoon all-purpose flour

Food groups

Servings

6-8

DIRECTIONS

1. Place lentils and 2 teaspoons salt in heatproof container. Cover with 4 cups boiling water and let soak for 30 minutes. Drain well.

2. Meanwhile, finely chop three-quarters of onion (you should have about 1 cup) and grate remaining quarter (you should have about 3 tablespoons). Heat 2 tablespoons oil in Dutch oven over medium heat until shimmering. Add chorizo and cook until browned on all sides, 6 to 8 minutes. Transfer chorizo to large plate. Reduce heat to low and add chopped onion, carrots, 1 tablespoon parsley, and 1 teaspoon salt. Cover and cook, stirring occasionally, until vegetables are very soft but not brown, 25 to 30 minutes. If vegetables begin to brown, add 1 tablespoon water to pot.

3. Add lentils and sherry vinegar to vegetables; increase heat to medium-high; and cook, stirring frequently, until vinegar starts to evaporate, 3 to 4 minutes. Add 7 cups water, chorizo, bay leaves, and cloves; bring to simmer. Reduce heat to low; cover; and cook until lentils are tender, about 30 minutes.

4. Heat remaining 3 tablespoons oil in small saucepan over medium heat until shimmering. Add paprika, grated onion, garlic, and 1/2 teaspoon pepper; cook, stirring constantly, until fragrant (about 2 minutes). Add flour and cook, stirring constantly, 1 minute longer. Remove chorizo and bay leaves from lentils. Stir paprika mixture into lentils and continue to cook for 10 to 15 minutes, until flavors have blended and soup has thickened. When chorizo is cool enough to handle, cut in half lengthwise, then cut each half into 1/4-inch-thick slices. Return chorizo to soup along with remaining 2 tablespoons parsley and heat through, about 1 minute. Season with salt, pepper, and up to 2 teaspoons sherry vinegar to taste, and serve.

COOKING TIPS

We prefer French green lentils, or lentilles du Puy, for this recipe, but it will work with any type of lentil except red or yellow. If Spanish-style chorizo is not available, kielbasa sausage can be substituted. Red wine vinegar can be substituted for the sherry vinegar. Smoked paprika comes in three varieties: sweet (dulce), bittersweet or medium hot (agridulce), and hot (picante). For this recipe, we prefer the sweet kind.

Make this soup up to 3 days in advance.

Indoor Pulled Chicken
with Sweet & Tangy BBQ Sauce

by Matthew Buchanan

SAUCE

1 1/2 cups ketchup

1/4 cup molasses

2 tablespoons Worcestershire sauce

1 tablespoon hot sauce

1/2 teaspoon salt

1/2 teaspoon pepper

CHICKEN

1 cup chicken broth

2 tablespoons molasses

1 tablespoon sugar

1 tablespoon liquid smoke

1 teaspoon unflavored gelatin

salt and pepper

2 pounds boneless, skinless chicken thighs, halved crosswise

hot sauce

Food groups

Servings

6-8

DIRECTIONS

1. For the sauce, whisk all ingredients together in a bowl and set aside.

2. Bring broth, molasses, sugar, 2 teaspoons liquid smoke, gelatin, and 1 teaspoon salt to boil in large Dutch oven over high heat, stirring to dissolve sugar. Add chicken and return to simmer. Reduce heat to medium-low, cover, and cook, stirring occasionally, until chicken is easily shredded with fork, about 25 minutes.

3. Transfer chicken to medium bowl and set aside. Strain cooking liquid through fine-mesh strainer set over bowl (do not wash pot). Let liquid settle for 5 minutes; skim fat from surface. Set aside fat and defatted liquid.

4. Using tongs, squeeze chicken until shredded into bite-size pieces. Transfer chicken, 1 cup sauce, 1/2 cup reserved defatted liquid, 3 tablespoons reserved fat, and remaining 1 teaspoon liquid smoke to now-empty pot. Cook mixture over medium heat, stirring frequently, until liquid has been absorbed and exterior of meat appears dry, about 5 minutes. Season with salt, pepper, and hot sauce to taste. Serve, passing remaining sauce separately.

Our indoor pulled chicken mimics the texture and flavor of outdoor slow-smoked pulled chicken in just a fraction of the time. We start by braising boneless, skinless chicken thighs in a mixture of chicken broth, salt, sugar, molasses, gelatin, and liquid smoke, which simulates the flavor of traditional smoked chicken. The gelatin and broth help mimic the unctuous texture and intense chicken flavor of whole chicken parts. To mimic the richness of skin-on chicken, we skip trimming the fat from the thighs and add the rendered fat back to the finished pulled chicken. Finally, we mix the shredded meat with some of the barbecue sauce and cook it briefly to drive off excess moisture.

— Matthew Buchanan of Leaning Pear

#1 Miso Matzo Ball Soup

by Eric Tanaka

DASHI (BROTH)

4 cups water

3 dried shiitake mushrooms

1 clove garlic

1 sheet kombu (dried kelp)

1 tablespoon white soy sauce

4 tablespoons red miso paste

1/2 cup chopped kale

MATZO BALLS

2 eggs

1/3 cup seltzer water

2 tablespoons olive oil

2 tablespoons grated parmesan cheese

Ground pepper to season

1/2 cup matzo meal

Food groups

Servings

2

PREPARE THE DASHI

1. Place water, shiitakes, and garlic in a 2-quart saucepan and simmer for 45 minutes or until shiitakes are soft.

2. Turn off the heat and add the kombu. Steep for 30 minutes.

3. Strain the mushrooms and return the dashi to the pan.

4. Slice the shiitakes and marinate in the soy sauce.

MAKE THE MATZO BALLS

5. In a bowl, stir together the first five ingredients for the matzo balls. Add the meal and mix into a batter. Refrigerate for 1 hour.

ASSEMBLE THE SOUP

6. Return the dashi to the stove. Whisk in red miso paste and bring to a simmer.

7. Form 2 equal balls or 6 smaller balls from the matzo batter and add to the miso-dashi broth. Simmer for up to 30 minutes.

8. Add chopped kale to 2 bowls. Ladle soup and matzo balls into the bowl and top with the marinated shiitakes.

Zuppa Pavese
(Pavia's Poached Egg Soup)

by Mary Ann Espositio from *Ciao Italia Pronto*

SAUCE

4 tablespoons butter

4 thick slices ciabatta bread

4 large eggs

4 tablespoons grated Parmigiano-Reggiano cheese

4 cups boiling hot beef or chicken broth (preferably homemade)

2 tablespoons minced parsley

Entrées

Food groups

Servings

4

45

DIRECTIONS

1. Preheat the oven to 350°F.

2. Melt butter in a nonstick pan and fry the bread slices until golden. Place each slice of toast in four individual oven-to-table soup bowls.

3. Crack an egg on top of each slice of toast and sprinkle each with a tablespoon of cheese. Carefully pour 1 cup of broth down the side of each bowl.

4. Set the bowls on a rimmed baking sheet. Place the sheet in the oven for 7 to 8 minutes or until the eggs have just solidified and are lightly poached.

5. Remove the baking sheet from the oven. Sprinkle the eggs with salt and pepper to taste; sprinkle parsley over the tops and serve.

Pavia is an ancient town in southwest Lombardy that is an important fertile area for the production of dairy products, including famous gorgonzola cheese. Not so well known is this nutritious soup which can be made in minutes. Use good country-style bread with an open crumb such as ciabatta, as well as the freshest eggs and the clearest beef or chicken broth.

— Mary Ann Espositio of *Ciao Italia*

Spaghetti Alla Carbonara
(Coal Miner-Style)

by Mary Ann Espositio from *Ciao Italia Five-Ingredient Favorites*

INGREDIENTS

1 tablespoon olive oil

4 ounces chunk pancetta, diced

1/2 pound spaghetti

3 large eggs, room temperature, lightly beaten

3/4 cup grated Parmigiano-Reggiano cheese

a good grind of coarse black pepper

salt to taste

Food groups

Servings

4

DIRECTIONS

1. Heat the olive oil in a small sauté pan and stir in the pancetta. Cook until crispy. Set aside and keep warm.

2. Cook the spaghetti in 4 quarts of rapidly boiling, salted water until it is al dente. Al dente means that the spaghetti is still firm, but no uncooked flour is visible when a strand is broken in half.

3. Drain the spaghetti in a colander, saving 2 tablespoons of the water. Immediately return the spaghetti to the pot and, keeping the heat very low, rapidly stir in the eggs, reserved water, and half the cheese. Combine well. Add the reserved pancetta and any drippings. Stir well. Add a good grind of pepper.

4. Transfer to a platter and sprinkle with the remaining cheese. Serve immediately.

COOKING TIPS

Just about everyone I know has a recipe for spaghetti alla carbonara. This simple but heavenly dish is said to get its name from the coal miners who could easily make it with readily available ingredients—eggs, cheese, and guanciale (cured and salted pig's jowl and cheeks). A likely story, but the fact is that this dish is superb when made correctly and a completely balanced meal. The eggs should be of the highest quality and at room temperature so they will mix well with the spaghetti. The cheese should be none other than true Parmigiano-Reggiano or Pecorino Romano. Today, the more readily available pancetta is used in place of guanciale. A pepper mill is essential for the right grind of black pepper.

Blissful Pea
Coriander & Coconut Soup

by Skye Craig

INGREDIENTS

2 tablespoons ghee
(clarified butter)

4 yellow onions, finely
chopped

1/2 head garlic, finely
chopped

bunch of fresh coriander,
bottom half of bunch finely
chopped and leaves picked

pinch of cayenne pepper,
plus more to taste

bunch of spinach, finely
chopped

3 cups frozen peas

1 1/2 13.5 ounce cans
coconut milk

4 cups water

Food groups

Servings

2

DIRECTIONS

1. Scoop ghee into a large saucepan over medium-low heat. Add the onions and saute for around 15 minutes. Stir in cayenne pepper, garlic, and coriander stems.

2. Sauté for a couple minutes, just long enough for everything to soften up. Add coconut milk and water, then bring to a simmer before adding peas and spinach.

3. Simmer just long enough for the peas to heat up, 2 to 3 minutes. Immediately remove the soup from heat and puree with a stick blender. Add more water if you want to thin the soup out.

4. Taste and add more salt and cayenne pepper if needed.

5. Serve sprinkled with toasted almonds, toasted sunflower seeds, pan-fried tofu cubes, Thai basil leaves, or fresh coriander leaves.

This is my all-time favourite soup for healing the nervous system and brain while receiving treatment. Loaded with nourishing ghee and phytonutrients from green vegetables, it's super quick to make and is packed full of flavor...heaven in a bowl, dear friends. Wishing you deep healing and happiness with every spoonful.

— Skye Craig of Master Chef Australia

Red Curry
Sweet Potato Soup

by Blake Pope

INGREDIENTS

1 cup olive oil

1/2 pound carrots, cut into 1-inch cubes

1 onion, julienned

1 tablespoon salt

1 tablespoon red curry paste

1/4 ounce garlic cloves, whole

5 pounds sweet potatoes, peeled and cut into 1-inch cubes

one 13.6-ounce can coconut milk

5 cups water

Food groups

Servings

4

DIRECTIONS

1. In a large stockpot, heat olive oil over medium heat. Add carrots, onions, and salt. Cook over medium heat until onions become translucent, about 20 minutes.

2. Add the curry paste and garlic cloves to the pan and cook for 3 minutes. Add sweet potatoes.

3. Add coconut milk and water.

4. Bring to a simmer and cook until the sweet potatoes are soft and fall apart.

5. Remove pot from heat and puree in a blender until smooth. If you find the soup is too thick, thin out with more water.

Pork Belly & Kimchi Stew

by Chris Shepherd

STEW

1/4 cup canola oil

2 ounces garlic cloves, whole

1 gallon water

2 ounces rice vinegar

6 ounces gochujang paste

4 ounces soy sauce

14 ounces Korean rice dumplings

8 ounces kimchi

2 pounds medium shrimp, peeled and deveined

green onions and benne seed, for garnish

PORK BELLY

one 4-pound skinless pork belly

1/4 cup canola oil

2 tablespoons salt

4 tablespoons cracked pepper

8 tablespoons chopped garlic

Food groups

Servings

4

ROAST THE PORK BELLY

1. Rub the pork belly with oil, salt, pepper, and garlic and let marinate overnight.

2. Preheat oven to 300°F.

3. Place pork belly on a rack in a roasting pan. Cover with plastic wrap and aluminum foil.

4. Place in oven and cook for 5 hours.

5. Remove pork belly from oven and pan. Chill in refrigerator.

6. Once cold, cut pork belly into 1-by-3-inch pieces.

MAKE THE STEW

7. In a large stock pot over medium-high heat, add the oil and toast the whole garlic cloves.

8. Add the water, vinegar, and gochujang. Simmer for 30 minutes.

9. Season with soy sauce. Add the rice dumplings and simmer for 30 minutes, stirring occasionally.

10. Add the kimchi.

11. Add the pork belly and simmer an additional 30 minutes.

12. Add the shrimp and simmer for 5 minutes.

13. Serve in large bowl and top with green onions and benne seed.

Charred Chicken
over Papaya Salad

by Chris Shepherd

CHICKEN

1 cup Red Boat fish sauce

1/4 cup honey

Juice of 4 limes, plus 2 limes for garnish

10 garlic cloves

2 bunches green onions

1 bunch cilantro, plus more for garnish

2 jalapeños

1/4 cup canola oil

1 whole chicken, 1 to 3 pounds

SALAD

1 green papaya

2 garlic cloves

1 Thai chili, stemmed and thinly sliced (use more, if you like heat)

5 cherry tomatoes

2 tablespoons Red Boat fish sauce

2 tablespoons sugar

1/2 lime, quartered

1/2 cup dried shrimp

1 tablespoon toasted peanuts

Food groups

Servings

4

GRILL THE CHICKEN

1. Place the fish sauce, honey, lime juice, garlic, green onion, cilantro, jalapeños, and oil in a blender. Puree to a smooth consistency. Place the raw chicken and sauce in a large resealable bag. Marinate 4 to 6 hours or overnight.

2. Prepare a medium-hot charcoal grill by oiling the grates. Place the chicken skin side down and grill for 3 to 5 minutes, being careful not to let it burn. The sugars from the honey will start to caramelize. Flip the chicken, move it to a cooler spot on the grill, and continue to cook until it reaches an internal temperature of 165°F. Transfer the chicken to a cutting board and let it rest for 10 minutes.

3. Carve the chicken: Cut the wing portion from the breast, cut the breast into 2 pieces and separate the leg and thigh.

PREPARE THE SALAD

4. Peel the outer skin of the papaya. Using a papaya shredder, shred the papaya into thin strips and place in a large bowl.

5. In a separate bowl, mix the garlic, chili, tomatoes, fish sauce, sugar, lime, and dried shrimp. Mix while lightly pounding the ingredients, causing them to bruise and release their flavors.

6. Add about a handful of the shredded papaya and continue mixing.

7. Top with toasted peanuts.

8. Arrange the chicken over a bed of papaya salad. Garnish with cilantro and lime wedges.

Rice-Seared Trout with
Mandarin Hazelnut Brown Butter

by Chris Shepherd

TROUT

4 3-ounce portions trout, with skin on

1 cup jasmine rice

salt and cracked pepper

2 ounces olive oil

SAUCE

1 1/2 ounces Red Boat fish sauce

1 1/2 ounces lime juice

1 1/2 ounces water

1 teaspoon ginger, grated with a microplane

1/2 teaspoon garlic, grated with a microplane

4 ounces butter

2 tablespoons ginger, julienned

1 mandarin, segmented

12 mint leaves

12 cilantro leaves

4 tablespoons hazelnuts, toasted and chopped

cracked black pepper

Food groups

Servings

4

COOK THE TROUT

1. Take raw jasmine rice and puree in a blender until it is a powder.

2. Toast the rice powder over low heat in a dry sauté pan until lightly brown, and reserve until ready to sear.

3. Season fish with salt and pepper, and crust with the toasted rice powder on the skin side.

4. Heat a cast iron pan over medium-low heat. When hot, add the olive oil to coat and look for little wisps of smoke to tell if it is hot enough to sear the fish. Gently add the fish skin side down, pressing until the fish skin flattens out. Add the remaining portions in the same manner.

5. Cook the fish to medium rare (about 70% done on the skin side), flip over in the pan for about 10 seconds, and place on a warm plate.

MAKE THE SAUCE

6. Before the trout is finished, combine the fish sauce, lime juice, water, grated ginger, and garlic and mix well.

7. In a small saucepan, brown the butter, starting from a cold pan over medium heat. Once the butter is brown, remove the pan from the heat and add the julienned ginger to aromatize. After about 10 seconds, add the fish sauce mixture and quick-simmer to lightly emulsify. Follow with the mandarins, mint, cilantro, and toasted hazelnuts.

8. Immediately spoon finished sauce over the trout and serve.

Chicken Thigh Roulade
with Mushroom & Tarragon Jus

by Michou Cornu

INGREDIENTS

4 boneless skinless chicken thighs

1 pound crimini mushrooms, sliced

2 ounces olive oil or butter

1 tablespoon chopped garlic

1 tablespoon chopped parsley

1 zucchini, julienned

2 to 3 branches tarragon, chopped

Salt and cracked pepper

Food groups

Servings

4

DIRECTIONS

1. Preheat oven to 395°F.

2. Pound the chicken thighs thinly between two sheets of plastic wrap. Set aside.

3. Sauté the mushrooms with olive oil or butter. When mushrooms are golden brown (about 5 minutes), add the garlic. Sauté another three minutes, then add parsley and seasoning to taste. Set aside and let cool.

4. Spread four 12-by-12-inch sheets of aluminum foil with butter or a little olive oil.

5. Place a little chopped tarragon and salt and pepper to taste on one of the sheets of foil. Lay a pounded chicken thigh in the center of the sheet; add some julienned zucchini and some of the prepared mushrooms. Roll the chicken very tightly and wrap it in the foil.

6. Repeat with the other chicken thighs.

7. Place each piece of rolled chicken on a baking sheet and bake for 14 minutes, then let chicken rest for 5 minutes.

8. Cut each end of the foil packages and unroll the foil. There will be natural juice coming out of the packages.

9. Cut each piece of chicken in two diagonal pieces and add some of the juice over the top.

Filet with Spinach

by Michou Cornu

INGREDIENTS

handful baby spinach leaves

shiso or basil

white fish filet

olive oil or butter (optional)

fresh herbs (optional)

cracked pepper

salt (optional)

Food groups

Servings

1

DIRECTIONS

1. Place baby spinach leaves, shiso or basil, a little pepper, and salt (if you want) on a plate.

2. Optionally, add a splash of olive oil or pat of butter for richness.

3. Cover the plate and heat in the microwave for 1 1/2 minutes.

4. Take the plate out and let it rest 3–4 minutes, then remove the cover. Bon appetit!

Colorado Lamb Dip
on Goat Cheese Biscuits

by Jennifer Jasinski

BISCUITS

1 1/2 pounds all-purpose flour

2 tablespoons baking powder

1 teaspoon kosher salt

1/4 cup sugar

1 1/2 tbsp chopped rosemary

6 ounces very cold butter, diced

8 ounces goat cheese, crumbled small

1 1/4 cups buttermilk

3/4 cup whole milk

LAMB

1/2 cup pure olive oil

6 sprigs rosemary, chopped

12 cloves garlic, chopped

1 whole leg of lamb, deboned

salt & cracked pepper

arugula

SAUCE

1/4 cup extra-virgin olive oil

reserved lamb trimmings

1/2 cup shallots, sliced

1/4 cup garlic, sliced

2 tomatoes, diced

1 tablespoon tomatoes, diced

1 tablespoon thyme leaves

1 teaspoon black peppercorns

1 cup red wine

1 quart veal demi-glace

salt & cracked pepper, to taste

Food groups

Servings

8

MAKE THE BISCUITS

1. In a bowl, mix together the dry ingredients, including rosemary.

2. Add the diced butter to the bowl, rubbing it into the flour with your hands so it is in pea-sized specks. Do the same with the goat cheese.

3. Add the buttermilk and milk all at once, mixing just enough to make the dough come together. Do not overmix.

4. Preheat oven to 400°.

5. Turn the dough out onto a lightly floured work surface and roll it out about 1 inch thick. Make a 4-fold by turning the 2 outside edges together into the center and then folding the entire piece of dough up like a book. Roll out again to 1 inch thick. Next, do a 3-fold (folding like a trifold wallet).

6. Roll out the dough about 1 inch thick. Using a 3-inch cutter, cut the biscuits. Transfer them to a parchment paper-lined baking pan and brush the dough with a bit of buttermilk; sprinkle the top of each biscuit with salt. Bake them in the 400° oven until puffed and golden brown (about 18 minutes). Depending on your oven, you may need to turn the tray once for even browning.

COOKING TIPS

Don't toss your scraps! Press them together and use them again. They won't rise quite as much, but they'll still be delicious. To work ahead, you can prepare the dough, refrigerate it or freeze it, storing it for over a week. Just cut and bake.

You can also make the lamb sauce and biscuit dough a day ahead. Just be sure to bake the biscuits on the day you plan to serve them.

GRILL THE LAMB

7. Preheat grill to high.

8. Rub the oil, chopped rosemary, and garlic all over the lamb and let it marinate at least 1 hour.

9. Season the lamb well with salt and black pepper. Grill the lamb medium-rare. Wait for the lamb to completely cool and then, using a sharp slicing knife, shave the meat as thinly as possible. Reserve trimmings for sauce.

COOK THE SAUCE

10. In a saucepot over medium heat, brown the olive oil and reserved lamb trimmings.

11. Add the shallots and garlic and cook until golden. Then add the tomatoes and stir until pulpy. Add thyme and peppercorns, then deglaze the pan with red wine. Reduce until the wine is syrupy.

12. Add the veal demi-glace to the pot and bring it to a simmer, skimming the impurities away as needed until the flavors have melded and the sauce is a desirable consistency to coat the lamb. Strain the sauce through a fine-mesh strainer and season to taste with salt and pepper. Hold warm until ready to sauce cooked lamb.

ASSEMBLE

13. Preheat the grill to medium.

14. Warm the goat cheese rosemary biscuits on the grill.

15. Cut each warm biscuit in half.

16. In a pan over medium heat, quickly warm up 1/2 cup lamb per biscuit (for a total of 8 cups of shaved lamb) in just enough lamb stock to reheat the meat.

17. When just warm, so the lamb stays medium-rare, remove the lamb from the stock and reserve the liquid.

18. Place the lamb on the biscuit and top with arugula.

19. Pour the reserved stock in a small bowl for dipping and serve with root vegetable chips on the side!

Turkey Meatloaf
(Freezable)

by Seisuke Kamimura

MEATLOAF

2 tablespoons canola oil

1 cup onion, finely chopped

3/4 cup celery, finely chopped

3/4 cup carrots, finely chopped

5 cloves garlic, minced

1 teaspoon dried Italian seasoning, crushed

1 1/2 teaspoons kosher salt

1 teaspoon black pepper

2 pounds ground turkey, thigh meat, once through medium grinder plate

2 eggs

1/2 cup half-and-half

a handful of sundried tomatoes

1/2 cup ketchup

1 cup bread crumbs

1 cup chicken broth

THE GLAZE

1 medium onion, cut into 2-inch-long, 1/8-inch-thick slices

1 tablespoon canola oil

1/2 cup ketchup

1/2 cup chicken broth

1 tablespoon sugar

1/4 teaspoon granulated garlic

Food groups

Servings

4

PREPARE THE MEATLOAF

1. Preheat oven to 375°F.

2. Heat a large sauté pan over medium-high heat and add oil. Once the oil starts to smoke , add the vegetables and garlic. Cook vegetables until tender, about 5 to 8 minutes. Add the next 3 ingredients and cook for another minute. Remove from pan and cool in the refrigerator.

3. In a medium mixing bowl, combine eggs, half-and-half, sundried tomatoes, and ketchup, and set aside.

4. In a large mixing bowl, combine the cooled vegetables with the ground turkey and mix well. Add egg mixture into the turkey mixture, mix well, then fold in the bread crumbs.

5. Form the meat into a compacted large bread loaf shape and place in the middle of a lightly greased baking dish. Make sure the baking dish is large enough so there is space for a "moat" around the meat.

MAKE THE GLAZE

6. Sweat onions in a pan with oil until tender, about 5 minutes, then add sugar and cook for 2 more minutes. Add the rest of the glaze ingredients and simmer until thick, about 10 minutes. Set glaze aside until cool.

BAKE THE MEATLOAF

7. Pour 1 cup of chicken broth around the meatloaf. Cover evenly with the glaze and bake until the internal temperature is 165°, about 1 to 1 1/2 hours. Rotate pan once during cooking. Let the meatloaf rest for 15 minutes before serving.

COOKING TIPS

Add water to the pan approximately every 20 minutes to keep the meatloaf moist. Reserve 1/2 cup jus to serve over the meatloaf.

Baked Salmon
with Hazelnut Gremolata

by Thierry Rauturneau

GREMOLATA

3 ounces darkly-roasted hazelnuts, finely chopped

1/2 bunch fresh Italian parsley, chopped

2 stems fresh tarragon, chopped

1/4 cup bread crumbs (or panko), toasted

4 tablespoons shallots, finely chopped

1 teaspoon garlic, finely chopped

1/4 cup olive oil

Salt and cracked pepper

SALMON

Four 4-ounce portions skinned and boned wild salmon

2 tablespoons butter

2 cups chanterelle mushrooms, sliced

1 celery root, peeled and cut into matchsticks

Salt and cracked pepper

Food groups

Servings

4

DIRECTIONS

1. Preheat the oven to 350°F.

2. Grease baking sheet with olive oil and place salmon portions on sheet.

3. Mix all of the gremolata ingredients and spread, about a quarter-inch thick, on salmon.

4. Place sheet in oven and cook for 7 to 8 minutes.

5. Meanwhile, melt butter in a sauté pan until golden brown. Add mushrooms and cook for four to five minutes.

6. Add celery root and season with salt and pepper. Cook slowly for four to five minutes more. Toss ingredients every minute or so until celery root is tender.

7. Spoon a portion of mushroom and celery root mixture on a plate, and place a piece of salmon on top of the vegetables. Serve right away.

White Beans & Clams

by Shaun McCrain

INGREDIENTS

1 tablespoon olive oil

3 cloves minced garlic

4 pounds well-rinsed manila clams

2 tablespoons butter

1 can cannellini beans, rinsed and drained

dry white wine (splash)

2 cups cherry tomatoes, halved

1 bunch fresh basil leaves

1 dried Spanish chorizo, Palacios brand, cut into 1/4-inch cubes

zest of 1 lemon

grilled bread for dipping

Food groups

Servings

4

DIRECTIONS

1. Put olive oil and garlic in a lidded pan large enough to hold the clams in a flat layer.

2. Lightly toast garlic and then add clams, butter, white beans, and wine and cover. Cook until clams begin to open, approximately 2 to 3 minutes.

3. Add tomatoes, basil, and chorizo. Cover again and finish cooking until all clams are open.

4. Discard any unopened clams.

5. Add lemon zest and stir to incorporate.

6. Serve with toasted or grilled bread for the broth.

Dungeness Crab
with Fresh Corn Polenta

by Brady Williams

INGREDIENTS

1 quart Anson Mills grits (fine yellow)

5 quarts skim milk

salt, to taste

6 ears corn

butter

lemon

Espelette pepper (or red pepper)

100 grams clarified butter

salt

1 quart water

2 dungeness crabs

Food groups

Servings

4

DIRECTIONS

1. Bring skim milk to a simmer, add the grits, and stir until cooked. Add more skim milk as needed and season with salt to taste.

2. Cut kernels off the corn cobs.

3. Combine kernels with clarified butter in braise at 100°C for 10 minutes.

4. Steep cobs in simmering water for 30 minutes. Strain and reserve.

5. Cook in boiling salt water for 6 minutes, then allow to cool.

6. Before serving, take the chill off the crab with a touch of butter, corn stock, lemon, and Espelette pepper.

7. Combine fresh corn, corn stock, and polenta and stir until well incorporated. Finish with the freshly picked Dungeness crab.

Grilled Chocolate
Sandwich with Salted Caramel
Dipping Sauce

SANDWICH

4.5 ounces semi-sweet chocolate chips

4.5 ounces 70% cacao chocolate, chopped to the size of chips, if needed

6 ounces cream

1 tablespoon sugar

1 1/2 tablespoon cocoa powder

1/4 teaspoon salt, plus more for sprinkling on sandwiches

8 to 12 slices thick-cut French bread

DIPPING SAUCE

1 cup cream

3/4 cup sugar

1 teaspoon unsalted butter, at room temperature

1/2 teaspoon salt

Desserts

Food groups

Servings

4-6

MAKE THE GANACHE

1. Place chocolate chips and 70% cacao chocolate into a heat-resistant bowl.

2. Place cream, sugar, cocoa powder, and salt in a saucepan and heat to 165°F. Whisk until there are no lumps, then heat back up to 165°F.

3. Pour cream mixture over chocolate and whisk until combined. Let the ganache sit on the counter until cooled, about 4 hours.

MAKE THE DIPPING SAUCE

4. Warm the cream in a small saucepan over low heat.

5. Meanwhile, in a heavy, medium sauté pan, melt the sugar over medium heat. As the sugar begins to liquefy, stir continually, as it will begin to change color and caramelize rather rapidly. When the sugar has reached an even light-amber color, watch for a bit of smoke to rise from it—this shows the sugar is done being caramelized.

6. Immediately add the heated cream a little at a time, whisking after each addition.

7. Remove the pan from the heat and thoroughly whisk in the butter and salt, adding more salt if you prefer. Allow to cool completely.

GRILL & ASSEMBLE THE SANDWICHES

8. Spread the cooled ganache onto a slice of French bread (we like to use a rustic potato bread), sprinkle with a good finishing salt, and top with another piece of bread.

9. Butter or oil a skillet or sandwich press. Cook sandwich on both sides until the bread is evenly browned and the ganache is melted through.

10. Allow the sandwich to cool for a couple of minutes, then cut in half. Serve with the salted caramel dipping sauce.

COOKING TIPS

Caramelizing sugar can be dangerous as it is very hot and can burn you easily. Use caution and do not touch the sugar while it is cooking!

If you have leftover ganache, you can store it wrapped in the refrigerator, for up to two weeks.

Cucumber Panna Cotta

1/2 lemon, zested with a fine microplane

1/4 cup sugar, plus 2 tablespoons

1 1/2 cups cucumber juice

1 cup cream

Pinch of kosher salt

3 sheets gelatin

Desserts

Food groups

Servings

4-5

1. Rub lemon zest with sugar.

2. Add lemon zest and sugar to cucumber juice and cream in a saucepan. Bring to a slight simmer (180°) and turn heat off. Let steep for an hour at room temperature.

3. Strain out the lemon zest. Bloom gelatin in cold water for 8 minutes; squeeze dry and add to cream mixture.

4. Heat cream as gently and at as low a temperature as possible, just to dissolve the gelatin, stirring constantly.

5. Pour into a bowl and chill over an ice bath until beginning to thicken. Pour into molds or individual bowls and refrigerate at least 2 hours until set.

COOKING TIPS

We serve this panna cotta with some fresh diced cantaloupe tossed with a little honey on top.

Two-Minute Fig, Walnut
& Bee Pollen Ice Cream

INGREDIENTS

3 ripe bananas

2 teaspoons bee pollen

2 dried figs

2 tablespoons tahini

handful of walnuts

sesame seeds

Food groups

Servings

2+

1. Cut ripe bananas into small pieces and freeze in an airtight container for several hours or overnight. Bananas can be stored for up to 3 months. When you're ready to make this delicious dairy-free ice cream, remove the fruit from your freezer.

2. Puree all ingredients in the blender until smooth. Serve in a dish and garnish with walnuts, sesame seeds, and extra bee pollen.

COOKING TIPS

Bee pollen is the most nutrient-rich food on the planet. If you can't afford vitamins, try bee pollen! Be sure to monitor your intake of bee pollen if you don't eat it regularly. You'll need to start with, say, 1/2 teaspoon and gradually increase to 2 teaspoons a day.

A study was done at the University of Vienna on 25 women with uterine cancer. A few were given bee pollen in their diet and quickly developed much better antibody production. Their immune-system cells that fight cancer and red blood cells that can fight infections started to increase. They also suffered less of the dreadful side effects that accompany chemotherapy. Their hair loss was minimal and they suffered less nausea. Hence, these women also suffered less from insomnia. The group that did not receive bee pollen did not have the same relief.

Bee pollen, figs, bananas, tahini, sesame seeds, and walnuts also deeply nourish your tissues, the brain, and nervous system and are powerful sources for producing more "happy hormones" such as serotonin. This ice cream will literally make you smile.

— Skye Craig of *Master Chef Australia*

Goodship Pot
Chocolate Fondue

2 Goodship Deep Dark Chocolate bars (20 mg THC total, 5 mg per person)*

9 to 10 ounces chocolate chips

1/2 to 3/4 cup milk

2 tablespoons butter

1 tablespoon Grand Marnier

1 tablespoon vanilla extract

*For a non-THC version, simply leave these out

Food groups

Servings

4+

Desserts

1. 1. Heat chocolate and 1/2 cup milk in the microwave or a double boiler, over very low heat, stirring frequently. If the mixture is too thick or looks curdled, add more milk and stir until smooth.

2. 2. When all the chocolate is melted, add in the butter, Grand Marnier and vanilla, and stir to fully incorporate.

COOKING TIPS

The list of scrumptious and creative items to dip in warm, melted pot chocolate...there's no end in sight. Our craving started with fresh fruit. We got strawberries, blueberries, raspberries, grapes, bananas, and a pineapple, then chopped them up and created fresh fruit skewers for round one. Then we played with things like candied ginger and vanilla waffle cookies. We also decided to blow some minds by crushing up Goodship Snickerdoodle cookies and sprinkling those on some of the chocolate-dipped items. Delectable! To finish our dessert with more dessert, we decided we couldn't complete our pot-chocolate-dipping spectacular without some classic strawberries and marshmallows. We threw pretzels into this mix for an extra salty crunch. We also suggest trying this warm chocolate over your favorite ice cream, or to sweeten your morning coffee!

As much as you love to simply break open a Goodship package and pop that delicious treat into your mouth, you can't forget that there are always opportunities to take your Goodship experience to an even higher altitude. We love cooking with both Goodship chocolate and cookies, and are excited to start sharing our favorite recipes with you! Follow our recipe to warm the chocolate, and then dip in your favorite bites—from fresh fruit, to crackers, to candy. Sail away with this finger-licking fun!

This recipe is designed to serve 4, at about 5 mg per person, but you can adjust the amounts of Goodship pot chocolate versus regular chocolate to create more servings or a stronger fondue.

— Hot Cakes

Goodship Pot
Chocolate Cheesecake

FILLING

3.7-ounce bittersweet chocolate, chopped (aim for 70% cacao)

12 bars (6 ounces total) Goodship Deep Dark Chocolate Bars or Coffee and Dark Chocolate Bars (10 mg of THC per serving)

Four 8-ounce packages cream cheese, room temp

1 1/4 cups plus 2 tablespoons sugar

1 teaspoon salt

1/4 cup unsweetened cocoa powder

4 large eggs

CRUST

24 chocolate wafer cookies

1 tablespoon sugar

1/4 cup (1/2 stick) butter, melted

1 teaspoon cinnamon

TOPPING

3/4 cup whipping cream

6 ounces bittersweet chocolate, chopped (aim for 70% cacao)

1 tablespoon sugar

Food groups

Servings

12

PREPARE THE CRUST

1. Preheat oven to 350°F.

2. Butter a 9-inch-diameter springform pan with 3-inch-high sides.

3. Blend cookies in processor until finely ground; blend in sugar and cinnamon. Add melted butter and process until well blended.

4. Press crumbs evenly onto bottom (not sides) of prepared pan.

5. Bake just until set, about 5 minutes. Cool crust while preparing the filling. Maintain oven temperature.

MAKE THE FILLING

6. Stir all chopped chocolate in metal bowl set over saucepan of simmering water until melted and smooth. Remove bowl from over water; cool chocolate until lukewarm, but still pourable.

7. Blend cream cheese, salt, sugar, and cocoa powder in processor until smooth. Blend in eggs, one at a time. Mix in lukewarm chocolate.

8. Pour filling over crust and smooth the top. Bake until center is just set and appears dry, about 1 hour.

9. Cool 5 minutes. Run knife around sides of cake to loosen, then chill overnight.

MAKE THE TOPPING

10. Stir the cream, 6 ounces of chocolate, and the sugar in a heavy medium saucepan over low heat until smooth. Cool slightly.

11. Pour topping over the center of the cheesecake, spreading to within 1/2 inchof edge and filling any cracks.

12. Chill until topping is set, about 1 hour (can be made up to 3 days ahead—cover with foil and refrigerate). Release pan sides. Transfer cheesecake to platter.

Goodship Snickerdoodle
Apple Crisp

FILLING

3 to 4 large Granny Smith apples, peeled and thinly sliced

3 tablespoons butter, melted

2 tablespoons flour

1 tablespoon lemon juice

3 tablespoons milk

1/2 teaspoon vanilla extract

1/4 cup brown sugar

1/2 teaspoon ground cinnamon

1/8 teaspoon nutmeg

1/8 teaspoon ground ginger

1/4 teaspoon salt

CRUMB TOPPING

3 Goodship Cinnamon Snickerdoodle Cookies (10mg of THC per cookie)*

1/2 cup flour

1/2 cup old-fashioned oats

1/2 cup brown sugar

1/2 teaspoon baking powder

1/4 teaspoon ground cinnamon

1/4 teaspoon salt

1/3 cup unsalted butter, diced into small chunks

*for a THC-free version, substitute with any snickerdoodle cookie

Food groups

Servings

6

1. Preheat oven to 375°F.

2. Place the snickerdoodle cookies into a food processor and pulse to create crumbs. If you do not have a food processor, use a chef's knife to chop the cookies into 1/8- to 1/4-inch pieces.

3. In a medium-sized bowl, combine the other crumb topping ingredients with the snickerdoodle crumbs. Stir with a fork or pastry blender until mixed well. Refrigerate while you prepare the apple filling.

4. In a small bowl, combine melted butter and flour until well blended. Add lemon juice, milk, and vanilla, and stir well. Stir in brown sugar, spices, and salt. Pour butter mixture over apples and toss to coat.

5. Pour apple mixture into an 8x8 inch baking dish and spread into an even layer. Sprinkle crumb topping evenly over the apples. Bake for 30 to 35 minutes or until golden brown and top is set. Remove from oven and allow to cool for at least 10 minutes before serving.

6. Serve with vanilla ice cream, whipped cream, or caramel sauce.

COOKING TIPS

To make this recipe ahead of time, make the apple filling, adding a bit more lemon juice so the apples don't brown. Store the apple filling in an airtight container in the refrigerator for up to one day. Make the crumble topping and put it in a separate resealable bag in the refrigerator. When ready to bake, sprinkle the topping on the filling. Bake as directed.

Antioxidant Berry
Smoothie

by Skye Craig

INGREDIENTS

1/2 cup frozen or fresh berries of your choice

1 tablespoon Berry Superfood powder or protein powder

1 or 2 large bananas (depending on how sweet you want it)

handful of oats

1 tablespoon tahini

1 tablespoon coconut oil

1 cup of almond or coconut milk

handful of ice (optional)

Food groups

Servings

1

DIRECTIONS

1. Add all ingredients to a blender and blend until smooth.

2. Pour into a glass and enjoy immediately.

All you need is a blender and a few ingredients, and you've got yourself a healthy and utterly delish meal in two minutes. Berries are low in fructose and easier than many other fruits for you to digest—and there are plenty of the right fats in this smoothie to help you heal well. Celebrating your health and recovery with melting hugs to you from Australia.

— Skye Craig of *Master Chef Australia*

Belly Healer Juice

by Skye Craig

SAUCE

a few carrots

1/2 large beet

1- to 2-inch knob of fresh ginger

1/2 lemon

1 or 2 green apples

handful of kale stems, plus a few leaves if you like

Food groups

Servings

1

DIRECTIONS

1. Juice all ingredients.

2. Pour into a glass and enjoy immediately.

COOKING TIPS

Be sure to wash your fresh vegetables and fruit very carefully to get rid of dirt and other contaminants. This is important while receiving and recovering from chemotherapy.

NUTRITION HIGHLIGHTS

Beets: Rich in antioxidants, iron, calcium, and vitamins A and C (especially the leaves).

Carrots: Rich in antioxidants, carotenes, and vitamins A and C. Studies have found that flavonoid compounds in carrots help protect from skin, lung, and oral cavity cancers.

Lemons: Super-high in Vitamin C, antioxidants and immune boosters, and a good source of B-complex vitamins.

Green apples: Full of antioxidants, green apples secrete organic acids.

Banana Breeze

by Tom Macy

INGREDIENTS

2 ounces white rum

juice of 2 lime wedges

1/4 cup cream of coconut

1 whole banana, cut into
3-4 pieces

1 cup ice

banana slices and orange
wheels for garnish

Food groups

Servings

2

1. Combine all ingredients in blender.

2. Blend for 20 seconds.

3. Pour into a tiki mug, wine glass, or any suitably tropical vessel you have. Garnish with a banana slice and orange wheel.

COOKING TIPS

For a non-alcoholic version, use pineapple juice instead of rum and add the juice of an additional lime wedge.

Ginger & Mint Spiked
Arnold Palmer
by Tom Macy

INFUSED BOURBON

1 bag or 2 spoonfuls of loose mint tea

1 bag or 2 spoonfuls of loose ginger tea (lemon ginger tea works)

1 cup bourbon

COCKTAIL

2 ounces ginger-and-mint-tea-infused bourbon

3/4 ounce fresh lemon juice

1 ounce simple syrup

3 ounces ice water

lemon wheel and mint sprig for garnish

Food groups

Servings

2

1. Combine all ingredients in a glass over ice, and pour back and forth between two glasses 3 or 4 times.

2. Garnish with a lemon wheel and a mint sprig.